COVERS & SCRIPT
MONTYNERO

ART & COLORS
MIKE DOWLING

LETTERING
COMICRAFT'S JIMMY BETANCOURT

TITAN
COMICS

INTRODUCTION

I t all started at the Hi-Ex comic convention, nestled in the Scottish highlands on the banks of the river Ness. It was a wonderful event: relaxed but exciting; informal and unpretentious. Lovely people, warmed by the spring sun, creators and fans mingling as one, families and children soaking it all in without cynicism. It's still my favorite ever comic con.

It was just what I needed - because I was frustrated. I love comics with an irrational passion and I'd come to the con to try and reconnect to the things that brought me joy and satisfaction, rather than the things that made me money. I was so creatively frustrated, in fact, that I was willing to do more or less anything it took to make myself content. There was a restless ache within me to create a comic book, to create something personal, to create something I owned. I felt I wouldn't die happy unless I did it, and the thought of spending the next forty years wondering 'what if' and dying bitter and frustrated, and then haunting my descendants with pained and incoherent groaning about sequential storytelling was too much to bear.

In the spirit of full disclosure you should know that my wife was with child, which was truly joyous news! It was the kind of news that left you in a grinning stupor – that made you want to buy a top hat just so you could throw it in the air and dance like a loon. But it also seemed back then that we only had six months left to do something recklessly creative before beginning a new life of sober responsibility and financial prudence. Absolute bollocks, as it turned out, but a very powerful feeling at the time. And from that turbulent well of emotions sprang the G+ virus, the catalyst for our story.

I didn't care if no-one read the comic (though I'd rather they did) and I didn't care if it was financially and emotionally disastrous (though I'd prefer it wasn't). I was going to do this thing and to hell with the consequences.

I'd probably still be toiling away at it if I hadn't met the inestimable Mike Dowling who is a) a lovely bloke, and b) a much better comic artist than I am. Recognising your limitations and working with people more talented than yourself is the key to success, trust me.

So we made this comic together, and we put our heart and soul into it. For my own part I put everything I knew about life, creativity, sex, humour, art and music into a vast pot and stirred it around until it tasted like a great story.

I really hope you enjoy *Death Sentence*, but I don't mind if you don't. Because we did it, and I can die happy now.

Cheers,
Monty, Dundee, 2014

When you're making a comic, it's the easiest thing in the world to have someone fly, explode, or be superfast. Superpowers are the common language of the medium. Just as Eskimos have fifty words for snow, so the stories that can be written with this vocabulary are many and varied. But the extraordinary doesn't stand out on the comic page unless you make it do something else, something *other*. Something with a dynamic, resonant hook.

For *Death Sentence*, that hook is adding superpowers to sex, drugs, and rock'n'roll. Possibly in that order. And who among us doesn't love sex, drugs and rock'n'roll – as Mary Whitehouse may well not have said...? There's celebrity here, too – a deconstruction of the tabloid's love of excess, in a narrative with a loud, satirical punk edge.

Death Sentence's G+ Virus, that provides its contractee with superpowers, is a sexually-transmitted disease. Sex is in the very inception of the book (and it fills a great deal of the panels, too). It's a sharp, 21st Century idea. And the virus also gives the sufferer six months to live – now that's what writers call an 'elevator pitch'! Would you have superpowers if it meant you'd die in six months?

There's plainly a sharp mind behind the often surprisingly lyrical script. Montynero is that credited mind (the insane and egotistical bad guy's called Monty too; hmmm...) and *Death Sentence* is brilliantly depicted by Mike Dowling, whose accessible storytelling pleasingly never loses the characters amidst the debauchery and ultra-violence.

Lastly – any story only goes as far as its characters. *Death Sentence*'s cast can be largely obnoxious, but they have heart and soul, too.

Enjoy!

ROB WILLIAMS, March 2014

Rob Williams is the celebrated writer of such titles as *The Royals: Masters of War, Ordinary, 2000AD*, and Marvel's *Revolutionary War*.

CHAPTER LIST

"SEX RESHUFFLES LIFE'S CARDS: IT MAKES BEAUTIFUL GENIUSES WHO SURVIVE AND UGLY FOOLS WHO DO NOT. IT IS A CONVENIENT WAY TO BRING TOGETHER THE BEST AND PURGE THE WORST AND TO SEPARATE THE FATE OF GENES FROM THAT OF THOSE WHO CARRY THEM.

RECOMBINATION IS A REDEMPTION, WHICH, EACH GENERATION, REVERSES BIOLOGICAL DECAY. IN SOME WAYS, IT IS THE KEY TO IMMORTALITY; A FOUNTAIN OF ETERNAL YOUTH - NOT FOR THOSE WHO INDULGE IN IT, BUT FOR THE GENES THEY CARRY."

STEVE JONES, THE LANGUAGE OF THE GENES

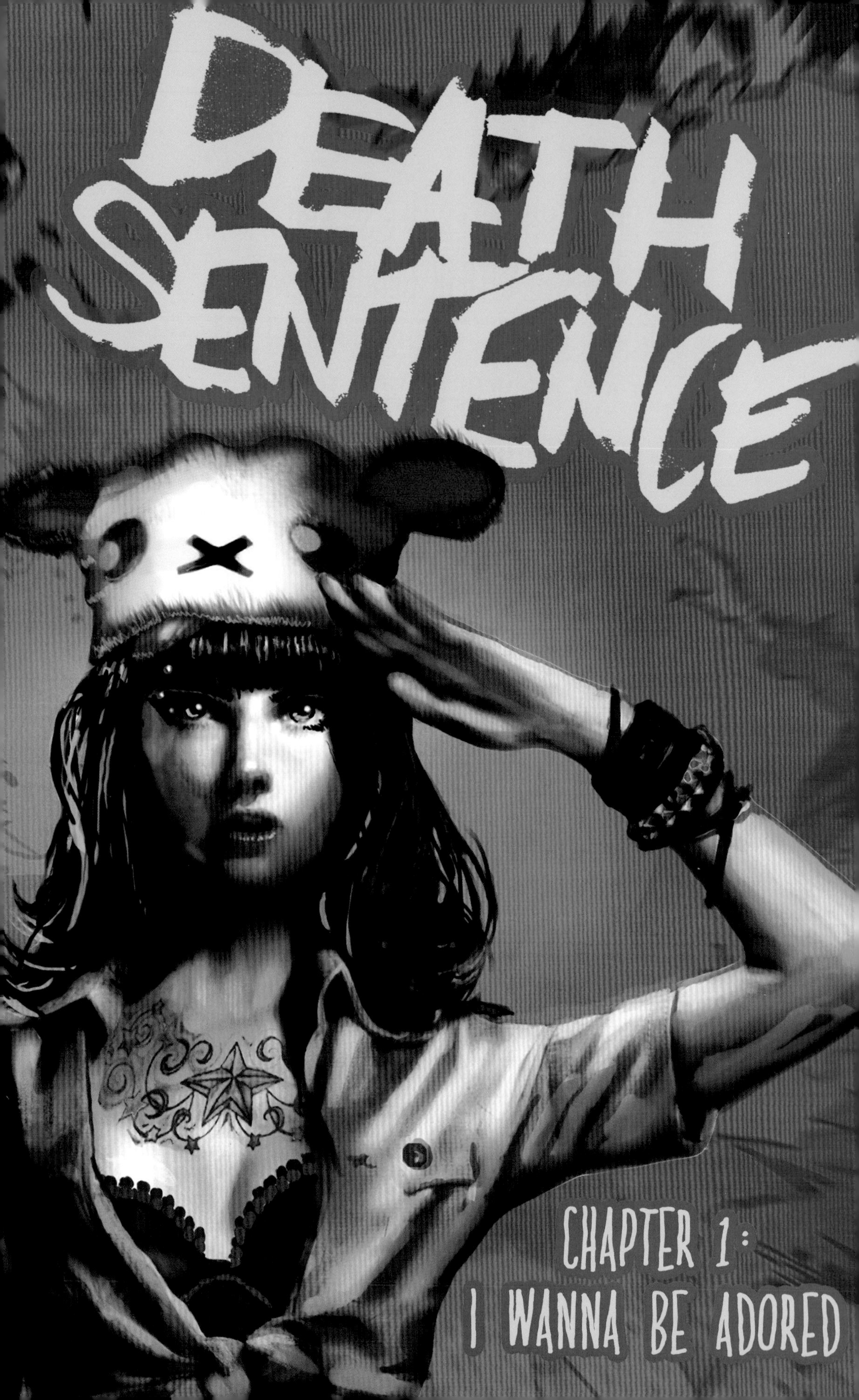
DEATH SENTENCE
CHAPTER 1:
I WANNA BE ADORED

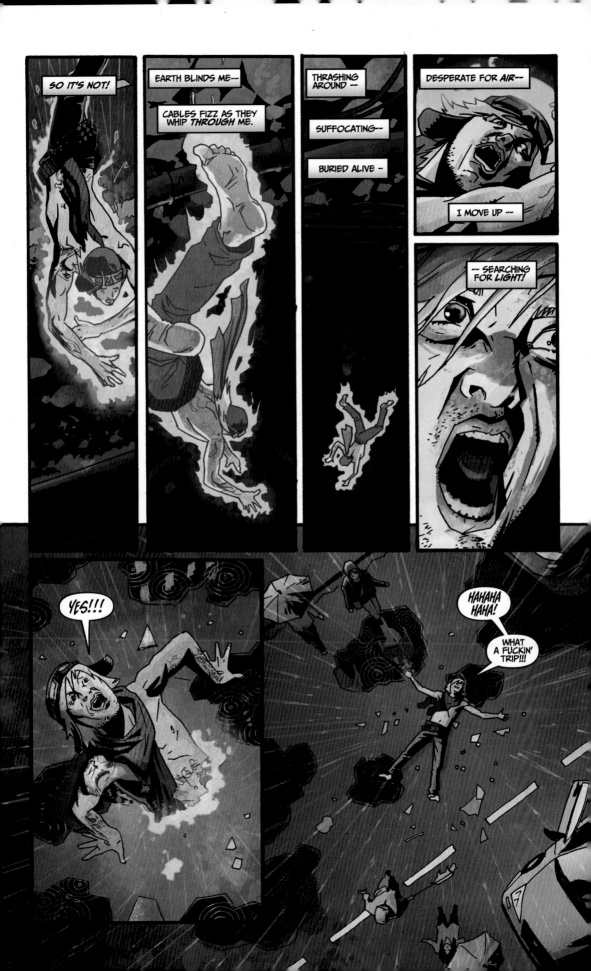

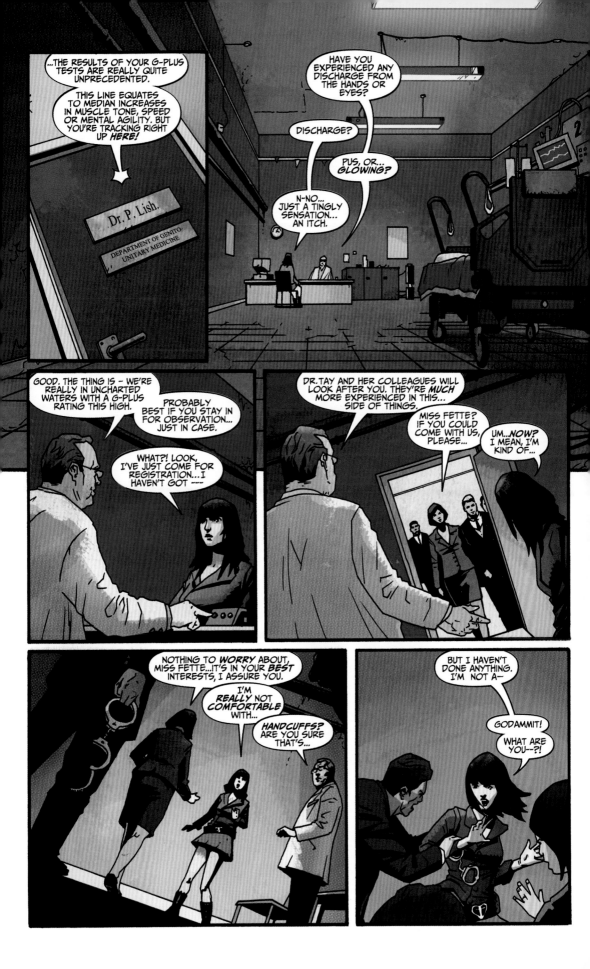

THE Post

HOME   SITE MAP   NEWS ALERTS

POP GOES THE WEASEL!

By ANDY LIVINGSTONE

The Post can confirm today that troubled junkie rocker Weasel – real name Danny Waissel – has just months to live, after contracting the deadly G-plus virus.

It's a bitter blow for the tormented star, following a widely-publicised battle with heroin and cocaine addiction and the break-up of his chart-topping band, 'The Whatever'.

Weasel's manager confirmed the shocking news in a press conference earlier today. The controversial singer-songwriter has abandoned work on his long-awaited solo album to tour the country and, "say goodbye to his loyal fans".

A source close to record company Sonic GBH pointed to more mercenary motives: "Everyone knows the record company backed the wrong horse in signing Weasel when the band broke up. They're just trying to recoup what they can in ticket sales and merchandise before he pops his clogs."

The tragic troubadour yesterday

Weasel is the fourth high-profile celebrity to contract the disease in the last month. The sexually-transmitted G-plus virus has swept across America and Europe, leaving thousands of fatalities in its wake. There is no known cure. Victims suffer enhanced skills and abilities in the final months of their tragically-shortened lives, leading to unprecedented feats of human accomplishment.

Millions watched in awe as G-plus American sprinter Tyrone Chambers broke the world 100m record by over 3 seconds at the Athens Olympic Stadium in March. And just twelve days later, grandmaster Alexei Amaund became the first person to triumph over supercomputer Deep Blue II in a celebrated 3-0 chess whitewash. Both men have since passed away.

DEATH SENTENCE

CHAPTER 2:
DISSOLVED GIRL

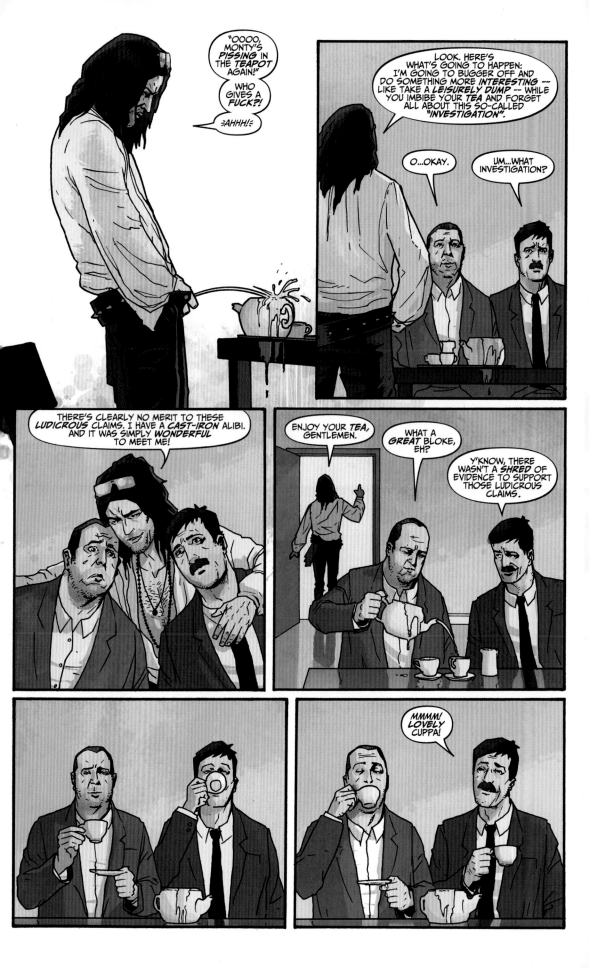

"If you want to make god laugh,
tell him your plans."
Woody Allen, b 1935

WEASEL INTERVIEW: 'Forever Fucked?'

Has he really kicked drugs? Has the tabloid hell over his G-Plus status taken its toll? Will we ever hear new material? In his 1st interview since the diagnosis, Weasel comes clean.

By Steve Maconie

Danny Waissel's trapped inside one of the most iconic faces of his generation. And there's no way out.

Once he seemed on the brink of rock immortality. Aged just 21 years old, and just a few weeks off the release of The Whatever's debut single 'Burnished Bits', he held in his chaotic mind the blueprint to shambolic poet-cum-rockstar 'Weasel' – iconic frontman of the biggest band in the country and hero to a pilled-up generation intent on partying themselves senseless.

Over the next three years the mainstream media convulsed with indignation as The Whatever pissed their outrageous sound into the ears of a nation's youth – a journey of such lunatic cloud-scraping ambition that it seems, in retrospect, to have been beamed in from a far more glorious reality. And at the centre of this decadent success stood one man, mouthing poetic verses soon to be on everyone's lips – that charismatic, throaty Lou Reed burr echoed by 300,000 disciples at Knebworth, soundtracking two summers on seminal album 'Bertram's Bakery' and its era-defining successor 'Bang the Tins' – bewitching millions with his bohemian swagger and androgynous sexual potency.

Then came the reckoning: the band broke up in bitter acrimony – co-writer and guitarist Axel Faff staking claim to the creative heart of the band, while Weasel languished in gaol after a succession of drugs offences. The model girlfriend left him; solo gigs descended into fights or tuneless chaos; accusations of plagiarism and creative bankruptcy loomed large from the shadows. An army of loyal fans kept the faith – but then came the cruelest of blows: a G-Plus diagnosis that leaves the brightest star of his generation with just six months to live. Is there any way back to past glories – or is Weasel now 'Forever Fucked'?

It's clear from the days **MNE** spent recording this interview that illness hasn't jolted Weasel into curing his addictions. On one memorable night he casually jizzed into a groupie's tits while snorting cocaine and swigging vodka from the bottle, barely pausing to formulate an answer to MNE's probing inquisition. The minstrel of mayhem has lost none of his decadence. And yet it's clear that this is not the drug-addled loon of last summer, refusing to censor the barely coherent rants and impassioned asides that bewildered his increasingly polarised audience. When we meet in The

Good Mixer Weasel looks lean and healthy, bantering wittily with the old men, tourists and hipsters crowding into the bar as word of his charismatic presence spreads. Beneath the battered flying helmet and red shemagh there's hope in those eyes, hope of salvation from the truest love of his life. The very thing that made us fall in love with him in the first place. Music.

It was John Lennon's birthday yesterday. Did you mark the day?

"'Course, man. I pulled an arty Japanese bird and we stayed in bed all day. She had a minge like a bear trapper's hat, so John would've felt right at home."

How do you feel about Axel's success since the band split? Three U.S. no. 1s, 2 Grammys, 4 Brits. And he wasn't exactly complimentary about you on 'Turtle's Head'.

"Couldn't care less, bruv. It's all sellout shit... sucking the man's cock. I ain't tongue buttering balls to get airplay, y'know? My shit is real shit. But Axel and me, we're like brothers, yeah? We have good times and bad times, but our shit runs deep. And I don't think he was singing about me there, y'know? Why would he?"

Well, you famously dissed him on your last single...

"Nah! The media misinterpreted that. I weave subtle layers, metaphors and allegories. My lyrics are like tone poems, open to many interpretations."

Even on 'Asshat Faff'?

"I'm talkin' about doors within doors, man. Transcending the obvious! Read between the lines, yeah? The message is there if you want to find it."

You're saying that we shouldn't take your work at face value?

"That's the beauty of my lyrics. The ambiguities are myriad. It's deep and open – just like his ass for Radio 1."

Have you changed your plans since the diagnosis?

"Yeah, I'm working on a lot more solo work. I'm buzzin' with ideas. It's now or never."

continued on page 48

WELL... LOOK.
WHY DON'T I READ
YOU A STORY, EH?
LIKE OLD TIMES --
HOW'S THAT?

YES!!

THEN
I'VE GOT
TO...

OH,
MAN, THIS IS
COMFY! THIS
IS *NICE!*

I'VE BEEN
SLEEPING
ON...
MMMM.
MAYBE
I COULD
JUST REST
A WHILE,
EH?

...GET A
LITTLE *≥HIC!≤*...
CATNAP--

MMMM!

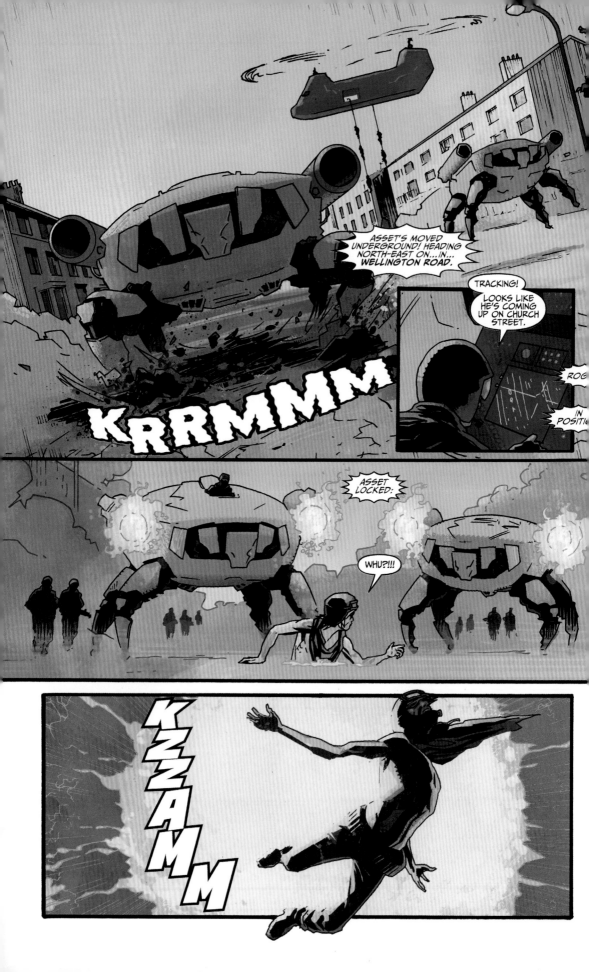

"It matters not how strait the gate,
How charged with punishments the scrol
I am the master of my fate:
I am the captain of my soul."

William Ernest Henley (1849-190

HOME | ABOUT | CONTACT

555-900-907
info@gplustestingcentre.com

Securing Your Future Health

G-Plus

HIV and Aids
Gonorrhea
Chlamydia
Hepatitis
Syphilis
Herpes

Do *you* think you are G-Plus?

1. Have you noticed an exponential increase in your physical or mental abilities?

2. Are you looking unusually youthful, or experiencing a glowing discharge from the eyes or fingers?

3. Have you caused or witnessed any extra-normal phenomena?

What Is G-Plus?
G-Plus is a fatal virus. Individuals infected will display extra-normal abilities. There is currently no cure or effective treatment for G-Plus. The virus is most prevalent in the major cities of America and Western Europe.

How Can G-Plus Be Transmitted?
G-Plus is most commonly transmitted through unprotected sexual activity. Those most at risk include young people within the 16-25 age group and sex workers.

Symptoms
Individuals with G-Plus may experience an increased sex-drive and an unusual discharge from the fingers and eyes. They become brighter, stronger or faster – and exhibit other unusual or extra-normal abilities.

Life expectancy for individuals with G-Plus is six months from the date the virus becomes productive. The virus can incubate for some time before this period. Individuals can expect to feel energetic and physically well until the final weeks, though depression or extreme swings in mood are not uncommon.

It is important to register and monitor each person with G-Plus to stop them becoming a danger to themselves or others. Failure to register is a criminal offence.
Counseling and assistance are available at your local STD ___ or ho___

Do you know someone who you suspect may have the G-Plus virus? Ring the anonymous advice line today: **555-900-907**

ENTER YOUR EMAIL: RACYMACY1992@HOTMAIL.COM
ENTER YOUR MESSAGE:

I SLEPT WITH THIS GUY AND NOW HE'S ALL OVER THE NEWS WITH G-PLUS.

I JUST HANDED MY ROOMIE A LIST OF COMPLAINTS ABOUT HER WACK BEHAVIOR AND STRAIGHT AWAY SHE GOT SICK. I THINK I MADE THE PAPER TOXIC? NOW I DON'T KNOW WHAT TO DO! PLEASE HELP!!

MACY

lustestingcentre.com/contactform

(!) CONTACT US
To ask us any question in complete confidence, click the link to open the secure form. One of our specially trained G-Plus medical staff will reply to your query within

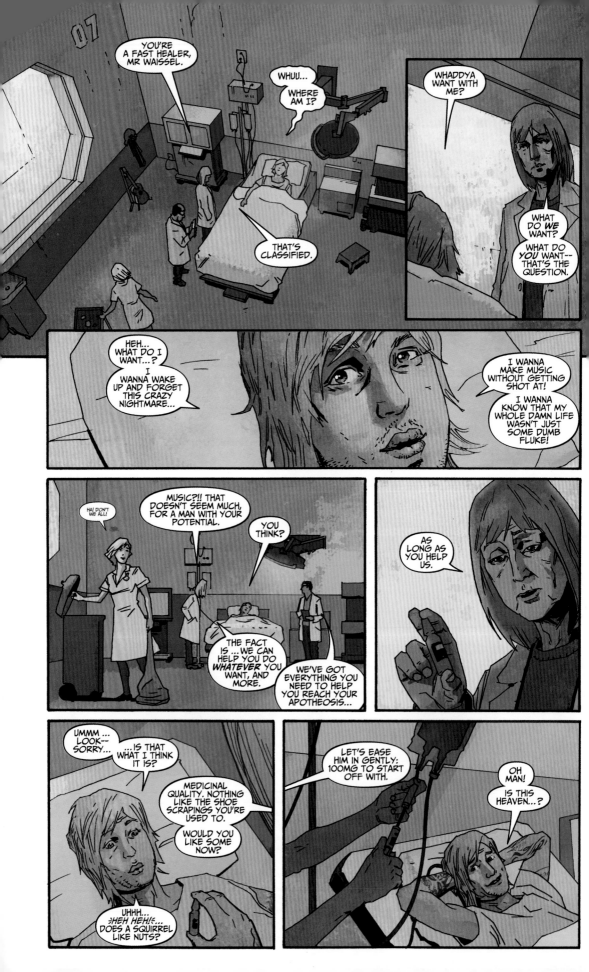

ARGGHH!

OH, I WOULDN'T WASTE TIME WITH A BAYONET, PRIME MINISTER.

KRAKK

IF YOU WANT TO *VANQUISH* AN ENEMY...

NOW LISTEN HERE. WHAT IS IT YOU WANT?

WE'RE IN THIS TOGETHER...WE CAN NEGOTIATE...

...PLEASE!?

...YOU SIMPLY CUT OFF ITS HEAD!!

HUHARRGH!!

MY HUMBLE APOLOGIES FOR THE MESS.

MAY I ENQUIRE... WHICH OF YOU ESTEEMED GENTLEMEN IS RESPONSIBLE FOR *BROADCASTING?*

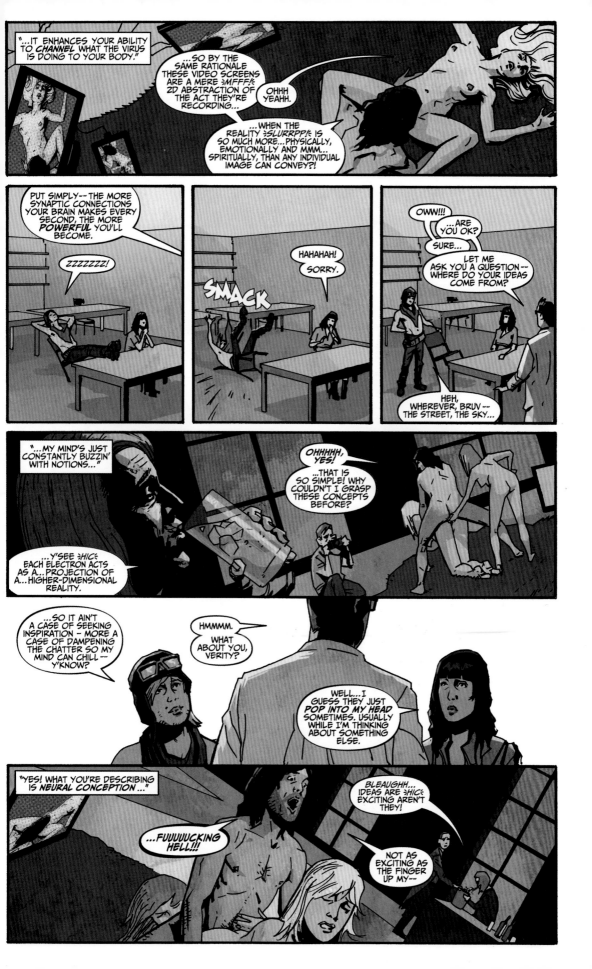

"Of all the forces that make for a better world, no is so indispensable, none so powerful, as hope."
Charles W. Sawyer (1868-1954)

Tue 03rd

I wake in a cold sweat,
pulse racing, mind whirring
— each breath a step closer
to the end. I'm dying — and no-one
can stop it happening...
You know the worst thing about
waking in the dead of night? That
blank half moment before memory
washes back like a dark tidal
swell. In that moment of emptiness you're not
truly alive. You're an automaton, neither doing
nor thinking — a bag of blood and gristle
and nerves and neurons. You're just a
gene machine built to breed and die,
another pointless vessel in a sea of meaningless.
So what do you do in the face of nihilism?
Invent God? Get shit-faced? End it all? Or
strive for purpose on purely mortal terms.
Create meaning right here, right now — on
earth? All my life I've dreamt great
paintings, epic landscapes, each stroke
growing with eloquent life. I'd wake
inspired — but then the memory would f   each
memory   lost somewhere slippery
           Whatever I painted could   er
     compare. So one day I gave up.   k a
design job, scratched a living.   dreams
worn away with each stroke g   mouse
     I just want to do something   onal
     before I go. A tiny piece g me   onahng
across the world that says 'Here I a   mean
something! I count. When I c   my
eyes and let my mind drift   e
     paintings come back to me
          shimmering and sway
               Taunting   with their

YOUR GOAL IS TO *BREAK* THE TARGET'S *CONCENTRATION* SO MY MEN CAN GET *CLOSE* ENOUGH TO TAKE HIM *DOWN* FOR GOOD.

THE U.S. NAVY WILL PROVIDE SUPPORTING FIRE, AND WE'LL BE WAITING ON THE *PERIMETER* FOR HIS *MIND CONTROL* TO DROP.

BREAK HIS *CONCENTRATION?!*... HOW THE *HELL* DO WE DO *THAT?*

BY PLACING ONE OF *THESE* ON HIS CRANIUM...

IT'S A NEURAL NEUTRALIZER – A *MINDBOMB* – SPECIFICALLY DESIGNED BY WILSON WRIGHT TO DISRUPT *BRAINWAVE* ACTIVITY.

GCHQ ARE *MONITORING* MONTY'S SPHERE OF AMBIENT *INFLUENCE.* IF HIS *EMPATHIC BROADCAST* DROPS OUT – EVEN FOR A *MINUTE* – WE'LL *ATTACK.*

YOU'VE GOT *EVERYTHING* YOU NEED TO *PREPARE.* GOOD LUCK!!!

HOW YOU FEELIN', V?

HONESTLY? I FEEL SCARED AND ANGRY, WEASEL.

HATE'S MY OVERWHELMING EMOTION RIGHT NOW... HATE AND *FRUSTRATION*...

...HATE FOR *MONTY*... FOR THE *VIRUS*... FOR THE *CHOICES* I'VE MADE...

HATE'S SOMETHING I'VE NEVER GIVEN *INTO* BEFORE. SHOULD SPARK A FEW *FRESH* IDEAS!

FUCK – YEAH! LETS ROLL WITH *HATE*...SEE WHERE THAT *LEADS*...

KRSMSSHH

Time: 1020

Name of Contact: ▮▮▮▮▮▮▮▮   Office/Division: ▮▮▮   Phone ▮▮▮▮▮

Address of Organization: ▮▮▮▮▮▮▮▮▮▮▮▮

Employee Name: ▮▮▮▮▮▮▮   Office/Division: IG   Phone #: ▮▮▮▮

Circle One
E/I

CALLED/VISITED DR. WILSON WRIGHT

Subject: INTERCEPT OF TRANSCRIPT

That was said:

FROM A ▮▮▮▮▮▮▮▮▮▮ THE FIELD OF ▮▮▮▮▮▮▮ AND
▮▮▮▮▮▮ IS FRAUGHT WITH DIFFICULTY. THE PROBLEMS ARE
WELL ESTABLISHED. FIRSTLY, A 'NEW' VIRUS IS SIMPLY THE SUBTLE
MUTATION OF AN EXISTING VIRUS, AND ONE THAT WILL SURELY MUTATE
AGAIN IN TIME. SECONDLY, A VIRUS AND ITS HOST ARE INTERDEPEN-
DENT. AS EACH VIRUS EVOLVES SO THE HUMAN BODY REFINES ITS DE-
FENCES, AN ENDLESS CYCLE OF ATTACK AND COUNTER THAT HAS PLAYED
OUT FOR GENERATIONS.

VIRUSES MUTATE BY VIRTUE OF ▮▮▮▮▮▮ RARE BUT INEVITABLE
ERRORS IN REPRODUCTION, ERRORS THAT OCCASIONALLY PROVE ▮▮▮▮
▮▮▮▮▮▮ SURVIVAL ▮▮▮▮▮▮▮▮▮▮▮▮
▮▮▮▮▮▮▮▮▮▮▮▮▮▮▮▮▮▮▮▮
▮▮▮▮▮▮▮▮▮▮▮▮▮▮▮▮▮

THE HOST ORGANISM REMAINS A ▮▮▮▮▮▮▮. IF THE VIRUS IS
TOO POTENT, THE HOST ORGANISM IS WIPED ▮▮▮▮▮▮▮ VIRUS
CAN SPREAD. IF THE ▮▮▮ IS TOO POWERFUL, THE VIRUS IS WIPED
OUT BEFORE TAKING HOLD. AN EFFECTIVE VIRUS THEREFORE NEEDS TO
EVOLVE IN BALANCE WITH THE DEFENCES OF HOST ORGANISMS, AN EVO-
LUTION THAT CANNOT BE ▮▮▮▮▮▮▮▮▮▮

VIRUSES EVOLVE FASTER THAN HUMANS, PRODUCING THOUSANDS OF OFF-
SPRING DAILY. THE AVERAGE WESTERN MAN HAS 2.4 DESCENDANTS
EVERY 20 OR MORE YEARS. IN NORMAL CIRCUMSTANCES IT WOULD

CNTD.

Reviewed by: ▮▮

VERITY, I--

...?!!

...WHAT THE FUCK DID YOU DO?!!

IT'S STILL THERE... I JUST CHANGED THE WAY *LIGHT* REFLECTS OFF IT.

OHHHHH!

All my adult life I've been fucking...

...quick sex, loving sex, angry sex, drunken sex --

-- scores of partners -- hundreds of positions...

...and only once have I made an emotional connection.

THIS MIGHT BE THE LAST TIME...

...MAKE IT COUNT.

He takes it slow...

...kissing every part of my body with a disciple's devotion...

...as if there's nothing in the world but us.

He's all I've got... the only one... the final one...

YES... LIKE THAT... JUST THERB!!

Only now do I realise the beautiful purpose of it all...

YES!

Sex...

...a reshuffling of the genetic cards...

...the redemption of recombination...

YES... YES...

...reversing the entropy of genetic decay with a brand new generation...

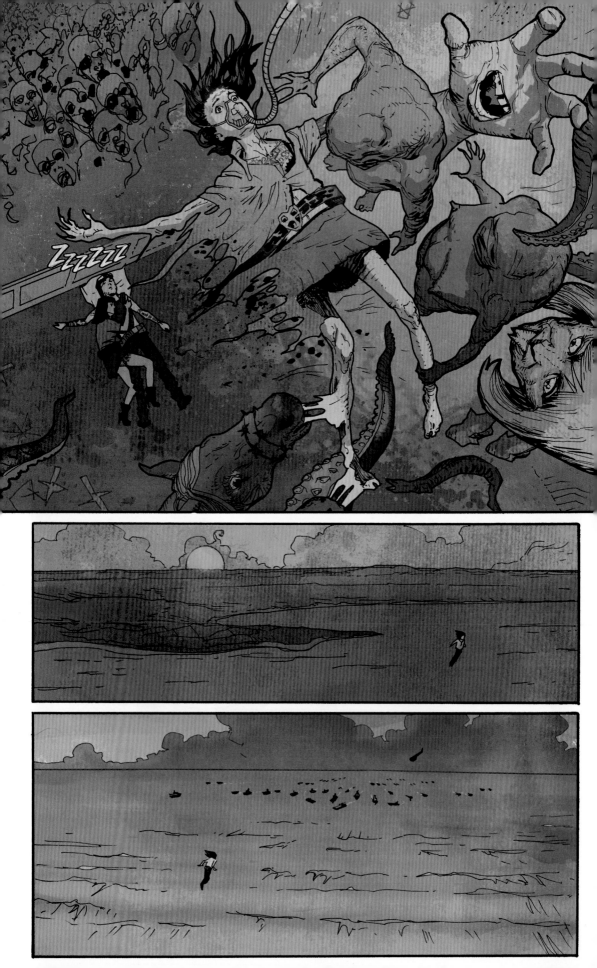

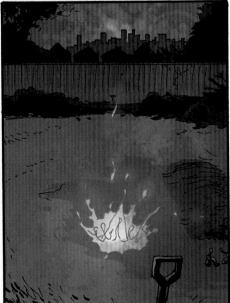

"IS ART LESS VALUABLE WHEN IT'S EPHEMERAL, RESONATING IN MEMORY: A FADING ECHO OF ITS ORIGINAL FORM? FOR SURELY SUCH ART STILL STIRS OUR EMOTIONS — AFFECTING US DEEPLY. AND WHAT MORE CAN GREAT ART DO?"

DEATH SENTENCE
BIOGRAPHIES

MONTY NERO

Monty writes and creates artwork for computer games (*SSX*, *Need for Speed*) and comics (Titan, Marvel, Vertigo, 2000AD). His agent for written work is James Wills at Watson, Little Ltd. He lives happily in Dundee, Scotland, with his wife and young daughter. You can find him on Twitter @ montynero and at www.montynero.com.

MIKE DOWLING

Mike Dowling lives with his family in Kent. As well as *Death Sentence*, he has worked on stories for 2000AD and Vertigo.

JIMMY BETANCOURT

Jimmy Betancourt has been lettering comics for the award-winning studio Comicraft for 12 years, proudly serving as part of Comicraft founder Richard Starkings' revolutionary army of fontmeisters and designers. When not showing off his skills as 'fastest letterer in the west' or watching the Lakers game, he's enjoying his time with his daughter Delaila in their home sweet home of Los Angeles.